THE COMMON UNITS OF MEASURE

WIPE-OFF BOOK

SCHOLASTIC INC.
New York   Toronto   London   Auckland   Sydney

HOW TO USE THIS BOOK

1. Look at the STUDY GUIDE on the opposite page.

2. Study the units of measure carefully.

3. Fold the flap on the back cover over the answers. Write your answers on the flap next to each question **with a grease pencil or an erasable felt-tip pen.**

4. Check your answers. How did you do?

5. If all the answers are correct, erase them with a damp cloth and move on to the next page.

6. If you have missed an answer, review the STUDY GUIDE page and try again.

ISBN 0-590-22282-1

Copyright © 1994 by FOUR HARTS, INC.

All rights reserved. Published by Scholastic Inc.

12 11 10 9 8 7 6 5 4 3 2 1   4 5 6 7 8 9/

Printed in the U.S.A.   1

First Scholastic printing, September 1994

STUDY GUIDE

Capacity:

3 teaspoons (t) = 1 tablespoon (T)
2 tablespoons (T) = 1 ounce (oz)
16 tablespoons (T) = 1 cup (c)
1 cup (c) = 8 ounces (oz)
2 cups (c) = 1 pint (pt)
1 pint (pt) = 16 ounces (oz)
4 cups (c) = 1 quart (qt)
2 pints (pt) = 1 quart (qt)
1 quart (qt) = 32 ounces (oz)
2 quarts (qt) = 1/2 gallon (gal)
1/2 gallon (gal) = 64 ounces (oz)
4 quarts (qt) = 1 gallon (gal)
1 gallon (gal) = 16 cups (c)
1 gallon (gal) = 128 ounces (oz)
1 liter (L) = 1,000 milliliters (ml)

Length:

12 inches (in) = 1 foot (ft)
3 feet (ft) = 1 yard (yd)
1 yard (yd) = 36 inches (in)
1 mile (mi) = 5,280 feet (ft)
1 mile (mi) = 1,760 yards (yd)
10 millimeters (mm) = 1 centimeter (cm)
10 centimeters (cm) = 1 decimeter (dm)
100 centimeters (cm) = 1 meter (m)
1 kilometer (km) = 1,000 meters (m)

Weight:

1 pound (lb) = 16 ounces (oz)
1 ton = 2,000 pounds (lb)
1 gram (gm) = 1,000 milligrams (mg)
1 kilogram (kg) = 1,000 grams (g)
1 metric ton = 1,000 kilograms (kg)

Temperature:

FAHRENHEIT	HINT:
Boiling - 212°	To convert Fahrenheit to Celsius, subtract 32, multiply by 5, and divide by 9.
Freezing - 32°	
CELSIUS	
Boiling - 100°	To convert Celsius to Fahrenheit, multiply by 9, divide by 5, and add 32.
Freezing - 0°	

C
A
P
A
C
I
T
Y

1 gal equals _____ qt   4

1 qt equals _____ c   4

8 T equals _____ c   1/2

2 T equals _____ oz   1

1 qt equals _____ pt   2

1 L equals _____ ml   1,000

1 pt equals _____ oz   16

16 c equals _____ gal   1

C
A
P
A
C
I
T
Y

4 oz equals _____ c   1/2

1 qt equals _____ oz   32

2 c equals _____ pt   1

1 T equals _____ t   3

1,000 ml equals _____ L   1

2 qt equals _____ gal   1/2

128 oz equals _____ gal   1

2 pt equals _____ qt   1

C A P A C I T Y

3 t equals _____ T   1

1 qt equals _____ pt   2

1/2 gal equals _____ oz   64

32 oz equals _____ qt   1

1 oz equals _____ T   2

4 c equals _____ qt   1

1/2 c equals _____ T   8

1 gal equals _____ c   16

C A P A C I T Y

1/2 c equals _____ oz   4

1/2 gal equals _____ qt   2

1 pt equals _____ c   2

1 gal equals _____ oz   128

1 pt equals _____ oz   16

4 qt equals _____ gal   1

64 oz equals _____ gal   1/2

1 qt equals _____ oz   32

L
E
N
G
T
H

1 ft equals _____ in   12

1 yd equals _____ in   36

10 mm equals _____ cm   1

1 m equals _____ cm   100

3 ft equals _____ yd   1

1 mi equals _____ ft   5,280

1 yd equals _____ ft   3

1 mi equals _____ yd   1,760

L
E
N
G
T
H

1,760 yd equals _____ mi   1

12 in equals _____ ft   1

1 cm equals _____ mm   10

5,280 ft equals _____ mi   1

100 cm equals _____ m   1

1,000 m equals _____ km   1

36 in equals _____ yd   1

1 dm equals _____ cm   10

W E I G H T

1 lb equals _____ oz	16
2,000 lb equals _____ ton	1
1,000 mg equals _____ g	1
1,000 g equals _____ kg	1
1 ton equals _____ lb	2,000
1 kg equals _____ g	1,000
8 oz equals _____ lb	1/2
1 metric ton equals _____ kg	1,000

TEMPERATURE

This thermometer reads
_____ °F   78
Could you wear a
short-sleeved shirt?
Yes or No   Yes

This thermometer reads
_____ °C   26
Could you build a snowman?
Yes or No   No

This thermometer reads
_____ °C   40
Could you swim outside?
Yes or No   Yes

This thermometer reads
_____ °F   41
Would you wear a
bathing suit?
Yes or No   No

This thermometer reads
_____ °F   35
Would you wear a heavy coat?
Yes or No   Yes

This thermometer reads
_____ °C   5
Should you wear a hat?
Yes or No   Yes

What unit of measure would you use to answer the following:

Would you use gallons or ounces to measure:

The water in a tub	gal
A glass of milk	oz
A bowl of rice	oz

Would you use feet or inches to measure the length of:

A couch	ft
A candy bar	in
A room	ft

Would you use pounds or ounces to measure the weight of:

A car	lb
A mouse	oz
A cat	lb

What unit of measure would you use to answer the following:

Would you use meters or centimeters to measure:

A big finger	cm
A football field	m
A house	m

Would you use liters or millimeters to measure:

A cup of coffee	ml
A fish tank	L
A glass of juice	ml

Would you use kilograms or grams to measure:

A desk	kg
A cookie	g
A bag or rocks	kg